MW00932157

GRANDMA
TELL ME YOUR STORY

A Guided Journal For Grandmothers To Share His Memories And Life Experience

PINE·TREE
PRESS

What's your name, where did it come from, and what does it mean?

_____
_____
_____
_____
_____
_____
_____
_____
_____
_____
_____
_____
_____

Where you named after someone?

_____
_____
_____
_____

Where and when were you born?

_____

_____

_____

_____

_____

How much did you weigh at birth?

_____

_____

_____

_____

_____

Did you have any birth defects?

_____

_____

_____

Put your baby picture here

What do you know about your family history/ancestry?`

_____
_____
_____
_____
_____
_____
_____
_____
_____
_____
_____
_____
_____
_____
_____
_____
_____
_____

Great-Grandfather   Great-Grandmother   Great-Grandfather   Great-Grandmother

Grandfather   Grandmother   Grandfather   Grandmother

Father   Mother

You

Sibling   Sibling   Sibling   Sibling

Family Tree

Put your family picture here

What cities did you live while growing up?

_____

_____

_____

_____

_____

_____

_____

What do you remember about this place?

_____

_____

_____

_____

_____

_____

What meals did you regularly eat growing up?

_____
_____
_____
_____
_____
_____
_____
_____
_____

What was your favorite food?

_____
_____
_____
_____
_____
_____
_____
_____

What did a typical mealtime look like?

_____
_____
_____
_____
_____
_____
_____
_____

What other special treats, meals, snacks, or other food did your family eat?

_____
_____
_____
_____
_____
_____
_____
_____
_____

Where did you go on vacation as a child?

_____

_____

_____

_____

_____

_____

_____

_____

What were your favorite places to visit?

_____

_____

_____

_____

_____

_____

_____

_____

What was your house like while growing up?

_____

_____

_____

_____

_____

_____

What was your bedroom like?

_____

_____

_____

_____

_____

What was your most precious childhood possession

_____

_____

_____

_____

_____

Who were your friends as a child?

_____

_____

_____

_____

_____

_____

_____

What was your favorite activity as a child?

_____

_____

_____

_____

_____

_____

_____

_____

_____

What did you not have as a child that we have today?

_____
_____
_____
_____
_____
_____
_____
_____
_____

What world event were significant to you as a child

_____
_____
_____
_____
_____
_____
_____
_____

What holidays did you celebrate and how did you celebrate it?

_____

_____

_____

_____

_____

_____

_____

_____

_____

_____

_____

_____

_____

_____

_____

_____

_____

_____

_____

Favorite holiday picture

What did you want to be/do when you grow up?

Did you become it?

What was the saddest moment of your childhood

_____

_____

_____

_____

_____

_____

_____

Did you ever feel lonely as a child? _____

_____

_____

Describe the time you felt the loneliest as a child?

_____

_____

_____

_____

_____

_____

_____

Favorite childhood pictures

What was your proudest moment of your childhood. Tell me about it.

_____

_____

_____

_____

_____

_____

_____

_____

_____

_____

_____

_____

_____

_____

_____

_____

_____

_____

_____

_____

What school did you attend as a child?

_____

_____

_____

Write about your earliest school memory?

_____

_____

_____

_____

_____

_____

_____

_____

_____

_____

_____

_____

_____

_____

_____

_____

_____

What was your favorite subject in school?

_____

_____

_____

_____

Who was your favorite teacher as a child?

_____

_____

_____

_____

_____

_____

_____

_____

What did you like about him/her?

_____

_____

_____

_____

_____

What sports or extracurricular activities were you involved in?

_____

_____

_____

_____

_____

_____

_____

_____

_____

_____

_____

_____

What did you most excel at as a child/teen/high school student?

_____

_____

_____

_____

_____

_____

What is your happiest moment as a teenager?

_____

_____

_____

_____

_____

_____

_____

_____

_____

_____

_____

Your saddest?

_____

_____

_____

_____

_____

Favorite teen years picture

What made you most nervous during your teenage years?

_____

_____

_____

_____

_____

_____

_____

_____

_____

_____

_____

_____

_____

_____

_____

_____

_____

_____

_____

How old were you when you learned to drive?

_____

_____

_____

_____

_____

_____

_____

_____

_____

_____

Who taught you how to drive?

_____

_____

_____

_____

_____

_____

_____

Who was your first crush?

_____

_____

_____

_____

_____

_____

_____

_____

_____

_____

_____

_____

Did the person like you back?

_____

_____

_____

_____

_____

_____

How did you learn about sex?

_____

_____

_____

_____

_____

_____

_____

_____

_____

_____

_____

_____

What advice would you give to somebody who just started dating?

_____

_____

_____

_____

_____

What was your first job?

_____

_____

_____

_____

How old were you back then? _____

_____

_____

What did you do, and how much were you paid?

_____

_____

_____

_____

_____

_____

_____

_____

_____

_____

_____

When did you first leave home?

_____

_____

_____

Write about your experience

_____

_____

_____

_____

_____

_____

_____

_____

_____

_____

_____

_____

_____

_____

_____

_____

What was the hardest part about growing up?

What was the best part about growing up?

_____

_____

_____

_____

_____

_____

_____

_____

_____

_____

_____

_____

_____

_____

_____

_____

_____

_____

Did you have any boyfriend as a youth?
Write about them

_____

_____

_____

_____

_____

_____

_____

_____

_____

_____

_____

_____

_____

_____

_____

_____

_____

_____

Who inspired you as you matured?

_____

_____

_____

_____

_____

_____

_____

_____

_____

_____

_____

_____

_____

_____

_____

_____

_____

What was the best part of your 20s

Picture from your 20s

What was the best part of your 30s?

_____

_____

_____

_____

_____

_____

_____

_____

_____

_____

_____

_____

_____

_____

_____

_____

_____

Picture from your 30s

Where is the most fascinating place you've visited?

Favorite holiday photo

Write about your dad. what do you like people to know about him.

_____

_____

_____

_____

_____

_____

_____

_____

_____

What was your relationship like with your dad?

_____

_____

_____

_____

_____

_____

Write about your mom. What do you want people to know about her?

_____

_____

_____

_____

_____

_____

_____

_____

_____

_____

_____

What was your relationship like with your mom?

_____

_____

_____

_____

_____

_____

_____

_____

Photo of your mom & Dad

What did your parents do for work?

What was your relationship like with your siblings?

_____

_____

_____

_____

_____

_____

_____

_____

What about your cousins and friends?

_____

_____

_____

_____

_____

_____

Picture of your siblings

What is your favorite family story?

Write about a funny story that has been passed through generations.

_____

_____

_____

_____

_____

_____

_____

_____

_____

_____

_____

_____

_____

_____

_____

_____

_____

_____

_____

_____

What do you remember about your grandparents?

_____

_____

_____

_____

_____

_____

_____

_____

_____

_____

What do you like people to know about them?

_____

_____

_____

_____

_____

_____

Grandparent's photos

How did you typically celebrate your birthday?

_____

_____

_____

_____

_____

_____

_____

_____

_____

_____

_____

_____

_____

_____

_____

_____

_____

Most memorable birthday photo

How did you meet grandpa?

_____

_____

_____

_____

_____

_____

_____

_____

_____

_____

_____

_____

_____

_____

_____

_____

_____

What was your first memory of him?

_____

_____

_____

_____

_____

_____

_____

_____

Where did you meet and when?

_____

_____

_____

_____

_____

_____

_____

_____

Photo of you & grandpa

When and how did you know that grandpa was the one?

_____

_____

_____

_____

_____

_____

_____

_____

_____

_____

_____

_____

_____

_____

_____

_____

_____

_____

_____

Did you want a big or small family?

_____

_____

_____

_____

_____

_____

_____

_____

_____

_____

_____

_____

_____

_____

_____

_____

_____

What are your memories about the birth of your first child?

_____

_____

_____

_____

_____

_____

_____

_____

_____

_____

_____

_____

_____

_____

_____

_____

_____

_____

_____

What are your happiest memory about being a first-time parent?

_____
_____
_____
_____
_____
_____
_____
_____
_____
_____
_____
_____
_____
_____
_____
_____
_____
_____
_____
_____

Photo of your first child

What was the most fun part about parenting?

_____

_____

_____

_____

_____

_____

_____

_____

What has been the hardest thing about parenting?

_____

_____

_____

_____

_____

_____

_____

_____

How has faith/spirituality/meditation played a role in your life?

_____

_____

_____

_____

_____

_____

_____

_____

_____

_____

_____

What are your personal superstitions?

_____

_____

_____

_____

_____

_____

How would you describe your personality?

_____

_____

_____

_____

_____

_____

_____

_____

_____

_____

_____

_____

_____

Are you an extrovert or introvert?

_____

_____

_____

_____

10 must read books youths should read before 30

_____

_____

_____

_____

_____

_____

_____

_____

_____

_____

Who are your favorite authors?

_____

_____

_____

_____

_____

_____

_____

_____

_____

What genre of music do you like listening to?

_____

_____

_____

_____

What are your favorite songs and artist

_____

_____

_____

_____

_____

_____

_____

_____

_____

How much is your taste in music based on what your friends like?

_____

_____

_____

_____

What are your greatest strength?

_____

_____

_____

_____

_____

_____

_____

_____

What are your greatest weakness?

_____

_____

_____

_____

_____

_____

_____

_____

What has been your greatest professional achievement?

_____

_____

_____

_____

_____

_____

_____

_____

_____

_____

_____

_____

_____

_____

_____

_____

_____

_____

_____

What has been your greatest personal achievement?

_____
_____
_____
_____
_____
_____
_____
_____
_____
_____
_____

What personal achievements make you proud?

_____
_____
_____
_____
_____
_____
_____

What do you do when you encounter obstacles to success?

_____

_____

_____

_____

_____

_____

_____

_____

_____

_____

.What are your secret survival strategies?

_____

_____

_____

_____

_____

_____

_____

_____

_____

How did you balance work and home life?

If you could have a do over, what would you change?

_____

_____

_____

_____

_____

_____

_____

_____

_____

_____

_____

_____

_____

_____

_____

_____

_____

What did you wish you knew before you were 30?

_____

_____

_____

_____

_____

_____

_____

_____

_____

_____

_____

_____

_____

_____

_____

_____

_____

_____

_____

What advice would you give to your teenage children?

_____

_____

_____

_____

_____

_____

_____

_____

_____

_____

_____

_____

_____

_____

_____

_____

_____

_____

_____

What advice would you give to your single children/grandchildren?

_____

_____

_____

_____

_____

_____

_____

_____

_____

_____

_____

_____

_____

_____

_____

_____

_____

_____

_____

_____

What advice would you give to your married children/grandchildren regarding marital relationship and parenting?

_____
_____
_____
_____
_____
_____
_____
_____
_____
_____
_____
_____
_____
_____
_____
_____
_____
_____
_____

What advice would you give to your children/grand children regarding life in general

_____

_____

_____

_____

_____

_____

_____

_____

_____

_____

_____

_____

_____

_____

_____

_____

_____

_____

_____

What life lesson helped you grow the very most?

_____

_____

_____

_____

_____

_____

_____

_____

How did it help you, and why?

_____

_____

_____

_____

_____

_____

_____

_____

How has your bucket list changed as you've grown older?

_____

_____

_____

_____

_____

_____

_____

_____

_____

_____

_____

_____

_____

_____

_____

_____

_____

_____

_____

What are you most proud of as an adult?

_____

_____

_____

_____

_____

_____

_____

_____

_____

_____

_____

_____

_____

_____

_____

_____

_____

_____

Can you remember one random act of kindness a stranger directed at you? What effect did it have on you?

_____

_____

_____

_____

_____

_____

_____

_____

_____

_____

_____

_____

_____

_____

When is the last time you did something nice for a stranger?

_____

_____

_____

_____

Do you have any regrets? What are they?

What might be different about you or your life if you no longer felt regret

_____

_____

_____

_____

_____

_____

_____

_____

_____

_____

_____

_____

_____

_____

_____

_____

_____

_____

_____

If you change three more things on your bucket list what would it be and why?

_____

_____

_____

_____

_____

_____

_____

_____

_____

_____

_____

_____

_____

_____

_____

_____

_____

_____

What is your personal philosophy?

_____

_____

_____

_____

_____

What motivates you?

_____

_____

_____

_____

_____

_____

What makes you happy?

_____

_____

_____

_____

_____

What advice would you give your younger self?

What legacy would you like to be known for?

_____
_____
_____
_____
_____
_____
_____
_____
_____
_____
_____
_____
_____
_____
_____
_____
_____
_____
_____

CPSIA information can be obtained
at www.ICGtesting.com
Printed in the USA
BVHW050730020723
666676BV00010B/971